Help with homework

English

revision

HI, MY NAME IS *KITCAT*...

... AND I'M *DIG*.

WE ARE HERE TO HELP YOU THROUGH THESE EXERCISES. START AT THE BEGINNING AND DON'T DO TOO MUCH IN ONE GO.

IT WON'T BE EASY ALL THE TIME – SOME PAGES CAN BE TRICKY – BUT WE'VE GIVEN YOU THE ANSWERS IN CASE YOU GET REALLY STUCK. NO PEEPING THOUGH! YOU WILL RECOGNISE A LOT OF THIS FROM THE WORK YOU DO AT SCHOOL (SORRY!). NOW YOU WISH YOU'D PAID MORE ATTENTION... **GOOD LUCK!**

Written by Nina Filipek
Designed and illustrated by Dan Green
Cover design by Dan Green

www.autumnchildrensbooks.co.uk

revise your spellings

stick a reward sticker here!

Read the word pairs. Tick the words that are spelled correctly.

always *or* allways

animul *or* animal

anuther *or* another

around *or* arownd

balloon *or* baloon

befor *or* before

being *or* bein

birthday *or* burthday

bruther *or* brother

can't *or* cant

chaing *or* change

children *or* childrun

comeing *or* coming

didn't *or* didnt

diffrent *or* different

does *or* dus

don't *or* dont

evry *or* every

father *or* fathir

first *or* furst

friend *or* frend

garden *or* gardan

gon *or* gone

great *or* grait

havf *or* half

head *or* hed

heard *or* hurd

I'm *or* Im

important *or* importent

jumped *or* jumpt

leave *or* leeve

light *or* lyte

money *or* munny

muther *or* mother

never *or* nevver

numbr *or* number

only *or* onely

uther *or* other

outside *or* owtside

paper *or* papeer

question *or* qestion

rownd *or* round

sisster *or* sister

sumthing *or* something

sometimes *or* somtimes

stopped *or* stoppt

suddenly *or* suddanly

swiming *or* swimming

thought *or* thowght

through *or* throuw

tried *or* tryed

usud *or* used

walked *or* walkt

white *or* whyte

whye *or* why

window *or* windoe

woke *or* woak

wurld *or* world

year *or* yeur

yung *or* young

difficult spellings

Learn to spell more difficult words by breaking them down into syllables.

remember:

Syllables are groups of sounds that you can hear in words.

For example:

Steg- o- saur- us

There are four syllables in Stegosaurus.

Learn to spell these words by breaking them into syllables:

information _____

beautiful _____

Saturday _____

February _____

LOOK, SAY, COVER, WRITE, CHECK: LOOK AT THE WORD, SAY IT, COVER IT, WRITE IT, CHECK IT.

Learn to spell words in groups. Underline the parts of these words that are tricky to remember, and learn to spell them.

famous	autograph
earring	solution
photograph	fabulous
pollution	stirring
jealous	paragraph
purring	position

Learn these 'ie' / 'ei' words:

field   receive

thief   ceiling

niece   seize —— 'S' SOUNDS LIKE 'C'

believe   eight

achieve   weight   'EI' SOUNDS LIKE 'AY'

retrieve   freight

friend   reign

There are a couple of exceptions to the rule, eg weird!
You will just have to learn to remember them.

remember:

'i' before 'e' except after 'c', or when it sounds like 'ay'.

THAT'S WEIRD!

remember:

Homonyms are words that sound the same but are spelled differently and have a different meaning.

Homonyms:

pear and pair   break and brake   there and their

right and write   where and wear   fair and fare

Make sure you know the different uses of these homonyms.

Now choose any four homonyms from the list and write a sentence for each.

1. _____

2. _____

3. _____

4. _____

stick a reward sticker here!

5

nouns, verbs and adjectives

Complete these sentences by adding nouns, verbs or adjectives.

1. I got a _____ for my birthday.

2. On Saturday, we are _____ to the _____.

3. I love _____.

4. Help! I'm _____.

remember:

Proper nouns are names of people, places (eg countries, cities, towns, rivers), days, months.

5. The _____ dog _____ its tail.

Re-write these sentences so that the proper nouns start with capital letters.

1. mrs jones is taking us swimming on friday.

_____

2. ben nevis is the highest mountain in great britain.

_____

3. The spanish flag is red and yellow.

_____

4. The river seine runs through paris, france.

_____

5. roald dahl is my sister annie's favourite author.

_____

Write some more nouns, proper nouns, verbs and adjectives here:

Nouns	Proper nouns	Verbs	Adjectives
_____	_____	_____	_____
_____	_____	_____	_____
_____	_____	_____	_____
_____	_____	_____	_____

Complete these collective nouns.

1. A shoal of _____

2. A flock of _____

3. A pack of _____

4. A crowd of _____

5. A pod of _____

> WHAT DOES A LITTER OF KITTENS AND A GAGGLE OF GEESE HAVE IN COMMON? A *LITTER* AND A *GAGGLE* ARE COLLECTIVE NOUNS.

Think of a synonym (a similar adjective) for each of the following words.

The first one has been done for you.

1. nice – good, pleasant, polite, okay _____

2. angry – _____

3. curious – _____

Think of an antonym (an opposite adjective) for each of these words.

1. disappointed – _____

2. excited – _____

3. perfect – _____

pronouns, adverbs and powerful verbs

stick a reward sticker here!

Read these sentences and decide which one sounds the most interesting.

WEAK VERB

1. The dog **went** across the road.

BETTER VERB

2. The dog **ran** across the road.

VERB + ADVERB

3. The dog **ran quickly** across the road.

POWERFUL VERB

4. The dog **dashed** across the road.

The sentence with the powerful verb is the most interesting. It is better to use one powerful word rather than lots of weaker ones.

Read the following text. Replace the weak verbs and adverbs (underlined) with powerful verbs and adverbs.

Choose from the following:
livid, approaching, dashed, apologised, secured, shouted, escaped

The dog <u>ran</u> across the road. A car was <u>coming</u> and the dog's owner <u>called</u> out to it. Luckily, the dog and the driver <u>didn't have any</u> injury but the driver was <u>very angry</u>. The owner <u>said he was sorry</u> and <u>put</u> the dog on its lead.

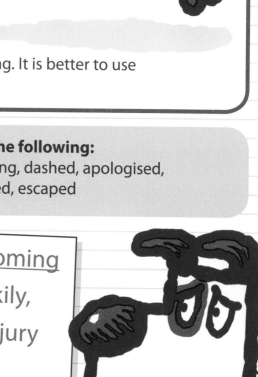

Write appropriate adverbs in the spaces below.
The first one has been done for you. Try to use a
different adverb each time.

1. The snow fell <u>softly</u>.

2. The dog growled _____.

3. The ice melted _____.

4. The leaves _____ rustled.

5. I walked _____ down the stairs.

6. My heart was beating _____.

7. Her hand gripped me _____.

8. I held on to the reins _____.

remember:

Adverbs tell us more about verbs. They often end in –ly.

remember:

These words are pronouns: I, he, she, it, we, us, you, they, them.

You can use pronouns to avoid repeating people's names in a text.

Write the missing pronouns in this story.
Then continue it in your own way:

Once upon a time, there was a nosy little girl called Goldie
Looks. _____ was walking down the street one day
(_____ was late for school, as usual) when _____ saw a
house. _____ had a grimy, dusty door. Goldie pushed the
door and _____ opened! Inside _____ saw three

_____

_____

_____

revise your punctuation

Punctuation helps the reader understand what is written. Writing is clearer when we write in sentences using full stops, capital letters, commas, semicolons, question marks, exclamation marks, speech marks, etc.

remember:

- A full stop (.) goes at the end of a sentence where we would pause.

- A comma (,) separates ideas within a sentence and items in a list.

- A semicolon (;) joins sentences or phrases that are closely connected.

- A colon (:) starts a list or a new idea.

- An apostrophe (') shows you who owns something. It also shows you where words have been shortened.

- A question mark (?) tells you that a question is being asked.

- An exclamation mark (!) shows surprise, humour or excitement.

- Speech marks (" ") tell you exactly what words are spoken.

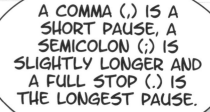

A COMMA (,) IS A SHORT PAUSE, A SEMICOLON (;) IS SLIGHTLY LONGER AND A FULL STOP (.) IS THE LONGEST PAUSE.

Will you read me a spooky story Tim asked

Only if you promise to go to sleep afterwards Tims dad replied

Yes I promise said Tim

His dad began to read It was almost midnight the light of the full moon brushed the trees…

Just when they got to the scariest part of the story all the lights went out

Then they heard a scary laugh Woah ah ah It was Mina Tims big sister playing a trick on them

Dad said Tim later I cant sleep Im too scared Can you read me something happy instead

remember:
Start a new paragraph for each new speaker. Begin writing the paragraph after leaving a space at the beginning of the line.

scary punctuation

Add the missing punctuation to these sentences.

1. The spell included the hair of a dog wings of a bat and a spiders web

2. Suddenly the door slammed shut

3. Its very dark in here she whispered

4. I think were trapped

5. Its a spell that I cant break she said

Use an apostrophe to shorten words in each of the sentences below.
The first one has been done for you.

6. I have written a ghost story.   I've written a ghost story.

7. It is so scary!

8. You will have to read it.

9. What is it called?

10. The witch could not do any magic!

WHICH WITCH WATCHES HER WAISTLINE?

Add the missing punctuation to the following story text:

Will you call him killer, like your auntys old cat she asked

No he is much more handsome than old killer ever was

Yes he really is quite a cutie, and he has such a sweet-tempered face and a softness around the eyes – why dont you call him kitty

you will need:

3 pairs of speech marks ☐ ☐ ☐

2 question marks ☐ ☐

2 full stops ☐ ☐

2 commas ☐ ☐

3 capital letters ☐ ☐ ☐

2 apostrophes ☐ ☐

Tick the boxes ☐ *as you find the missing punctuation.*

stick a reward sticker here!

1st, 2nd and 3rd person

The narrator is the person in the text who tells the story.

Change the pronouns (underlined) in this text from the first to the third person.

> <u>I</u> was now beginning to grow handsome; <u>my</u> coat had grown fine and soft, and was bright black. <u>I</u> had one white foot, and a pretty white star on <u>my</u> forehead.

Change the pronouns (underlined) in this text from the third person to the first person.

> At this time <u>he</u> used to stand in the stable, and <u>his</u> coat was brushed every day till it shone like a rook's wing. It was early in May, when there came a man from Squire Gordon's who took <u>him</u> away to the Hall.

Extracts from 'Black Beauty' by Anna Sewell.

'BLACK BEAUTY' IS WRITTEN IN THE FIRST PERSON: THE HORSE, BLACK BEAUTY, NARRATES THE STORY. STORIES WRITTEN IN THE FIRST PERSON ENCOURAGE THE READER TO EMPATHISE WITH THE MAIN CHARACTER.

Read this job advertisement. It is written in the second person.

IF **YOU** LOVE HORSES THEN THIS IS THE JOB FOR **YOU**!

You can...

- help muck out the stables each day.
- groom and feed the horses.
- have **your** riding lessons for free!

What are **you** waiting for? **You** can apply now!

remember:

The pronouns 'you' and 'your' are speaking directly to the reader. Advertisers like to use these pronouns because they are friendly and persuasive.

Now it's your turn to write. Continue the following text:

A diary – in first person

Today _____

_____

An instruction – in second person

This is what you do: _____

_____

A description – in third person

She/he looked like _____

_____

_____

_____

stick a reward sticker here!

limericks and poems

Use different colours to circle the words that rhyme.

EIGHT SYLLABLES

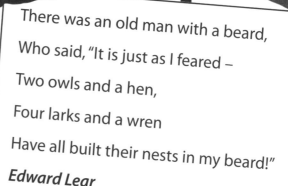

There was an old man from Peru
Who dreamed he was eating his shoe.
He woke in a fright
In the middle of the night
And found it was perfectly true!

Anon

There was an old man with a beard,
Who said, "It is just as I feared –
Two owls and a hen,
Four larks and a wren
Have all built their nests in my beard!"

Edward Lear

Make up a limerick about a pet, someone you know or yourself.

Base it on the examples above.

_____

_____

_____

remember:

A limerick is a humorous verse of five lines, with the rhyming pattern: a, a, b, b, a.

wow!

oops!

fab!

oh, no!

cool!

easy peasy!

nooo!

yes!!

woo!

oops!

wow!

yay!

brill!

lol

score!

woo!

yay!

yikes!

ok!

gr8!

yippee!

not bad!

great!

wicked!

cool!

ok!

brill!

fab!

cool!

ok!

brill!

fab!

yippee!

not bad!

great!

wicked!

yay!

yikes!

ok!

gr8!

wow!

oops!

fab!

oh, no!

cool!

easy peasy!

nooo!

yes!!

woo!

oops!

wow!

yay!

brill!

lol

score!

woo!

Poetry can make us laugh, make us cry, or make us think.

Read this classic poem.

Hurt no living thing.

Ladybird, nor butterfly,

Nor moth with dusty wing,

Nor cricket chirping cheerily,

Nor grasshopper so light of leap,

Nor dancing gnat, nor beetle fat,

Nor harmless worms that creep.

Christina Rossetti

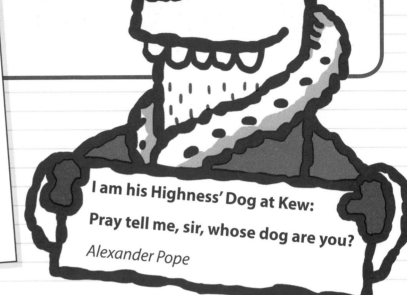

I am his Highness' Dog at Kew:

Pray tell me, sir, whose dog are you?

Alexander Pope

Write a poem in the style of 'Hurt no living thing'.
Choose your own animals and rhyming words.
Try to follow a similar rhyming pattern.

I KNOW THE SHORTEST POEM IN THE ENGLISH LANGUAGE. IT'S CALLED 'FLEAS'.

Fleas

Adam 'ad 'em.

_____

_____

_____

_____

_____

_____

_____

similes and metaphors

remember:

Similes are when you describe something as being <u>like</u> or <u>as</u> something else.

Similes:

The moon shone **like** a torch.

He felt as strong **as** an ox.

Make up some of your own similes to complete these descriptions.

1. Some dinosaurs were as tall as _____

2. The longest dinosaurs were as long as _____

3. The smallest dinosaurs were like _____

4. Some dinosaurs had teeth like _____

remember:

Metaphors are when you say that something <u>is</u> something else.

For example, when you say someone **is** a dinosaur – that's a metaphor. It means the person is old-fashioned!

Write your own metaphors to complete these descriptions.

1. She is a _____ in the swimming pool.

2. She is a _____ on the race track.

3. He is a _____ in the boxing ring.

4. He is a _____ on the skateboard.

personification

Personification:

The sun smiled.

The grey sky wept.

The waves roared.

The spooky house groaned.

remember:

Personification is when a writer gives human characteristics to a non-human thing. It is similar to a metaphor.

Make up some of your own personifications to complete these descriptions.

1. The road _____

2. The ships _____

3. The car _____

4. The computer _____

You can add an adjective before the noun if you want to.

POP!   BUZZ!   CRASH!   SQUELCH!   SQUEAK!

GLUG!   PLOP!

remember:

Onomatopoeia is a word that sounds like the thing it is describing.

Complete each sentence below using an onomatopoeic word. The first one has been done for you.

1. The water sloshed on the floor.

2. The door _____

3. The gate _____

4. The plate _____

stick a reward sticker here!

powerful prefixes and suffixes

remember:

A **prefix** is a group of letters at the beginning of a word.

A **suffix** is a group of letters at the end of a word.

These prefixes and suffixes can change the meaning of the root word to its exact opposite.

For example:

truth**ful**	thought**ful**	cloud**y**
untrue	thought**less**	cloud**less**

Write one word from each pair (above) in these sentences.

1. It was a grey and _____ day.

2. She behaved in a cruel and _____ way.

3. The thief lied. His statement was _____ .

Choose from the remaining words to complete these sentences.

1. It was a bright and _____ day.

2. She behaved in a kind and _____ way.

3. The thief told the truth. His statement was _____ .

Add the prefix dis- to change these words.

agree   honest   interested

disagree _____   _____   _____

like   obedient   advantage

_____   _____   _____

appear   continued   loyal

_____   _____   _____

Write three sentences using any of the dis- words above. You can change the tense (with a different suffix) if you prefer.

1. _____

2. _____

3. _____

Change these words to mean more than one.

baby   _____   wolf   _____

memory   _____   knife   _____

discovery   _____   child   _____

fox   _____   sheep   _____

cactus   _____   volcano _____

fungus   _____   tomato   _____

remember:

Suffixes can change words from singular to plural.

THERE ARE A COUPLE OF WORDS SET TO TEST YOU IN THIS LIST!

proverbs and idioms

Write what you think these proverbs mean.

1. Birds of a feather flock together.

_____

2. The early bird catches the worm.

_____

3. Put your best foot forward.

_____

4. Don't cry over spilt milk.

_____

5. It never rains but it pours.

_____

Write what you think these idioms mean.

over the moon _____

under the weather _____

in the same boat _____

touch and go _____

high and mighty _____

home and dry _____

Write these sentences using standard (formal) English.

1. I won you in that race.

_____

2. It was him what done it.

_____

3. Let me lend your book.

_____

4. I'm the bestest.

_____

5. Me and my sister was lost.

_____

6. We was scared.

_____

7. Thems my shoes.

_____

8. Here's the lunch what I bought.

_____

remember:
You should use standard English in your writing at school – except perhaps in story writing when you want to make a character's direct speech sound more realistic.

YOU NEED TO LEARN TO WRITE PROPER LIKE, INNIT!

borrowed words

Some words we use are borrowed from other languages – this sometimes makes them more difficult to spell!

Words derived from French:

café

restaurant

hotel

beauty

garage

village

Words derived from Greek:

dinosaur

aqua

alpha

amphibian

geography

biology

Words derived from Latin:

decimal

adventure

century

vice versa

example (eg)

etcetera (etc)

remember:

Many scientific words come from Latin or Greek.

IT'S ALL GREEK TO ME!

OTHER EXAMPLES ARE: ANNO DOMINI (AD), ANTE MERIDIEM (AM)! THAT'S WHY WE LIKE TO ABBREVIATE THEM!

stick a reward sticker here!

Write some sentences using any of the borrowed words above – or any other borrowed words you know.

1. _____

2. _____

3. _____

4. _____

terrible tenses

stick a reward sticker here!

remember:
Verbs change tense depending on when the action takes place.

For example:

To fly

Past: I flew

Present: I fly

Third person present: He/she flies

Present continuous: I am flying

Future: I will fly

To swim

Past: I swam

Present: I swim

Present (third person): He/she swims

Present continuous: I am swimming

Future: I will swim

Write the verbs in the correct tense.

To think

Past: I _____

Present: I _____

Present (third person): He/she _____

Present continuous: I am _____

Future: I will _____

To write

Past: I _____

Present: I _____

Present (third person): He/she _____

Present continuous: I am _____

Future: I will _____

To eat

Past: I _____

Present: I _____

Present (third person): He/she _____

Present continuous: I am _____

Future: I will _____

To make

Past: I _____

Present: I _____

Present (third person): He/she _____

Present continuous: I am _____

Future: I will _____

conjunctions

For example:

Kit loves sport. She hates swimming.

Kit loves sport **but** she hates swimming.

Conjunctions:

and	so	or	when
but	if	because	while

Use a conjunction to join two sentences into one sentence:

1. Dig and Kit are friends. They are always arguing.

_____

2. Kit usually wins. She shouts the loudest!

_____

3. Kit came home late last night. She's still asleep.

_____

4. Dig gets worried. Kit gets home late.

_____

For example: Kit snores when she is sleeping.

Kit snores is the main clause.

when she is sleeping is the subordinate clause.

Join each main clause to a subordinate clause to make one sentence with two clauses.

Main clause	Subordinate clause
1. Many mammals are intelligent	to hide from their enemies.
2. Baby mammals feed on their mother's milk	when they are born.
3. Some mammals have camouflage markings	and can learn to do new things.

Underline the main clause in each sentence below.

1. Mammals' bodies stay the same temperature whether it is hot or cold.

2. Some mammals grow a thicker coat in the winter months.

3. Some mammals like to live in groups when they are in the wild.

stick a
reward
sticker
here!

connectives

Connecting adverbs:

after	now	later	finally	however
then	next	suddenly	firstly	consequently

Put these sentences in the correct order.

Look for the connecting words to help you. Number the sentences from 1 to 8.

☐ Next, their tails become shorter.

1 Frogs lay their eggs, called 'frog spawn', in water.

☐ After a few weeks tiny tadpoles hatch.

☐ First they grow their back legs.

☐ They breathe through gills, like fish.

☐ Then they grow their front legs at about ten weeks old.

☐ Finally they can jump out of the water and breathe air!

☐ Now they look like tiny frogs.

TOP TIP FOR BUDDING AUTHORS: A FAMOUS AUTHOR ONCE SAID, IT'S EASY; ALL YOU HAVE TO DO IS "PUT THE RIGHT WORD IN THE RIGHT ORDER."

Now write out the sentences in the correct order below.

_____

_____

_____

_____

_____

_____

_____

stick a reward sticker here!

active and passive verbs

remember:
Some verbs can be **active** or **passive**.

For example:

The dog <u>chased</u> the cat. —— ACTIVE

The cat <u>was chased by</u> the dog. —— PASSIVE

The active sentence is about what the dog did.

The passive sentence is about what happened to the cat.

Draw a line from the active to the passive text.

1. The dog picked up the scent.

2. Tom read the poem.

3. The mother carried the baby.

4. Molly made the cake.

The cake was made by Molly.

The baby was carried by the mother.

The scent was picked up by the dog.

The poem was read by Tom.

Write these sentences as passive text.

1. The snake ate the mouse.

_____

2. Harry won the prize.

_____

3. Some insects drink pollen.

_____

4. Plants and animals need oxygen.

_____

5. The girl wrote the scary story.

_____

stick a reward sticker here!

29

testing times

1. Where could you add a **semicolon** in this text?

She opened the cage door slowly in the darkness she could just make out the outline of an animal.

2. Underline the **pronouns** in this text. Is it written in first, second or third person?

Text this number for your chance to win this week's bonus prize – a holiday for two in a resort of your choice!

3. Underline the word that **connects** these two sentences.

The detective suspected this was a lie. However, he didn't cross-examine the suspect at this point.

4. Write the missing **colon** in this text.

You need to decide between these colours red, yellow, blue or green.

5. Write a list of your favourite things here, adding **commas** and/or **semicolons** to separate each item in the list. Write 'and' before the last item and end with a full stop.

_____

6. Replace the verb (underlined) for a more **powerful verb**.

Dinosaurs <u>walked</u> the Earth 65 million years ago.

7. Write a phrase containing a **possessive apostrophe** for each of the following.

the dog belonging to the family   _____

the sweets belonging to Jack   _____

the books belonging to the girls   _____

the goal belonging to the players   _____

8. Write theses **contractions** in full.

wouldn't _____   he'll _____   it's _____

where's _____   that's _____   how's _____

answers

revise your spellings
These words are correct:

always	friend	question
animal	garden	round
another	gone	sister
around	great	something
balloon	half	sometimes
before	head	stopped
being	heard	suddenly
birthday	I'm	swimming
brother	important	thought
can't	jumped	through
change	leave	tried
children	light	used
coming	money	walked
didn't	mother	white
different	never	why
does	number	window
don't	only	woke
every	other	world
father	outside	year
first	paper	young

difficult spellings
in-form-a-tion
beaut-i-ful
Sat-ur-day
Feb-ru-a-ry

nouns, verbs and adjectives
1. Mrs Jones is taking us swimming on Friday.
2. Ben Nevis is the highest mountain in Great Britain.
3. The Spanish flag is red and yellow.
4. The River Seine runs through Paris, France.
5. Roald Dahl is my sister Annie's favourite author.

1. a shoal of fish
2. a flock of sheep
3. a pack of wolves
4. a crowd of people
5. a pod of dolphins

Here are some possible answers:
1. nice – good, pleasant, polite, okay
2. angry – cross, annoyed, livid
3. curious – interested, inquisitive, questioning

1. disappointed – pleased
2. excited – bored
3. perfect – imperfect

pronouns, adverbs and powerful verbs
The dog dashed across the road. A car was approaching and the dog's owner shouted out to it. Luckily, the dog and the driver escaped injury but the driver was livid. The owner apologised and secured the dog on its lead.

Once upon a time, there was a nosy little girl called Goldie Looks. She was walking down the street one day (she was late for school, as usual) when she saw a house. It had a grimy, dusty door. Goldie pushed the door and it opened! Inside she saw three …. (to be continued by you!)

revise your punctuation
"Will you read me a spooky story?" Tim asked.
"Only if you promise to go to sleep afterwards," Tim's dad replied.
"Yes, I promise," said Tim.
His dad began to read. "It was almost midnight; the light of the full moon brushed the trees…"

Just when they got to the scariest part of the story, all the lights went out!
Then they heard a scary laugh, "Woah-ah-ah!" It was Mina, Tim's big sister, playing a trick on them.
"Dad," said Tim later. "I can't sleep. I'm too scared. Can you read me something happy instead?"

scary punctuation
1. The spell included: the hair of a dog, wings of a bat and a spider's web.
2. Suddenly the door slammed shut!
3. "It's very dark in here," she whispered.
4. "I think we're trapped!"
5. "It's a spell that I can't break!" she said.
6. I've written a ghost story.
7. It's so scary!
8. You'll have to read it.
9. What's it called?
10. The witch couldn't do any magic!

punctuation test
"Will you call him Killer, like your aunty's old cat?" she asked.
"No, he is much more handsome than old Killer ever was."
"Yes, he really is quite a cutie, and he has such a sweet-tempered face and a softness around the eyes – why don't you call him Kitty?"

1st, 2nd and 3rd person
<u>He</u> was now beginning to grow handsome; <u>his</u> coat had grown fine and soft and was bright black. <u>He</u> had one white foot and a pretty white star on <u>his</u> forehead.

At this time <u>I</u> used to stand in the stable, and <u>my</u> coat was brushed every day till it shone like a rook's wing. It was early in May, when there came a man from Squire Gordon's who took <u>me</u> away to the Hall.

personification
Here are some possible answers:
1. The water sloshed on the floor.
2. The door slammed shut.
3. The gate creaked open.
4. The plate smashed.

powerful prefixes and suffixes
1. It was a grey and cloudy day.
2. She behaved in a cruel and thoughtless way.
3. The thief lied. His statement was untrue.

1. It was a bright and cloudless day.
2. She behaved in a kind and thoughtful way.
3. The thief told the truth. His statement was truthful.

disagree
dislike
disappear
dishonest
disobedient
discontinued
disinterested
disadvantage
disloyal

babies	wolves
memories	knives
discoveries	children
foxes	sheep
cacti	volcanoes
fungi	tomatoes

proverbs and idioms
1. People who share the same interests like to be together.
2. If you need to do something, do it straightaway.
3. Try your best.
4. Don't worry about things you can't change.
5. When bad things happen they come all at once.

Over the moon – feeling very happy
Under the weather – feeling unwell
In the same boat – in the same situation
Touch and go – risky
High and mighty – behaving as if important
Home and dry – safe

standard english
1. I beat you in that race.
2. He did it.
3. Let me borrow your book.
4. I'm the best.
5. My sister and I were lost.
6. We were scared.
7. They are my shoes.
8. Here's the lunch that I bought.

terrible tenses

I thought	I wrote
I think	I write
He/she thinks	He/she writes
I am thinking	I am writing
I will think	I will write

I ate	I made
I eat	I make
He/she eats	He/she makes
I am eating	I am making
I will eat	I will make

conjunctions
Here are some possible answers:
1. Dig and Kit are friends <u>but</u> they are always arguing.
2. Kit usually wins <u>because</u> she shouts the loudest!
3. Kit came home late last night <u>so</u> she's still asleep.
4. Dig gets worried <u>when</u> Kit gets home late.

conjunctions
1. Many mammals are intelligent and can learn to do new things.
2. Baby mammals feed on their mother's milk when they are born.
3. Some mammals have camouflage markings to hide from their enemies.

1. <u>Mammals' bodies stay the same temperature</u> whether it is hot or cold.
2. <u>Some mammals grow a thicker coat</u> in the winter months.
3. <u>Some mammals like to live in groups</u> when they are in the wild.

connectives
1 Frogs lay their eggs, called 'frog spawn', in water.
2 After a few weeks tiny tadpoles hatch.
3 They breathe through gills, like fish.
4 First they grow their back legs.
5 Then they grow their front legs at about ten weeks old.
6 Next, their tails become shorter.
7 Now they look like tiny frogs.
8 Finally they can jump out of the water and breathe air!

active and passive verbs

1. The dog picked up the scent.	The scent was picked up by the dog.
2. Tom read the poem.	The poem was read by Tom.
3. The mother carried the baby.	The baby was carried by the mother.
4. Molly made the cake.	The cake was made by Molly.

1. The mouse was eaten by the snake.
2. The prize was won by Harry.
3. Pollen is drunk by some insects.
4. Oxygen is needed by plants and animals.
5. The scary story was written by the girl.

testing times
1. She opened the cage door slowly; in the darkness she could just make out the outline of an animal.
2. It is written in the second person. Text this number for <u>your</u> chance to win this week's bonus prize – a holiday for two in a resort of <u>your</u> choice!
3. The detective suspected this was a lie. <u>However,</u> he didn't cross-examine the suspect at this point.
4. You need to decide between these colours: red, yellow, blue or green.
5. You can mark this one yourself!
6. Dinosaurs <u>roamed</u> the Earth 65 million years ago.
7. the family's dog, Jack's sweets, the girls' books, the players' goal
8. would not   he will   it is
   where is   that is   how is